Scorpio

Astrology Coloring Book

Color Your Zodiac Sign

The 12 Signs

Sign Symbols

ARIES

TAURUS

GEMINI

CANCER

LEO

VIRGO

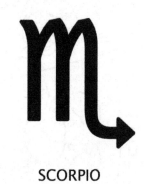

LIBRA

SCORPIO

SAGITTARIUS

CAPRICORN

AQUARIUS

PISCES

Scorpio

October 23 - November 22

SCORPIOS ARE KNOWN best for their assertive and passionate demeanor. They love facts and long for the truth in all situations. To them this is much more important than feelings. Although they are a water sign, and emotion is highly important to them, they show this in a different way. They are secretive, loyal, and once you get close to them they will never waver. Pluto, their ruler, is the planet of transformation. They make excellent leaders but are easily jealous and suspicious of others.

Symbol: Scorpion

Planet: Pluto

Element: Water

Color: Red

Traits: Resourceful, Brave, Passionate, Stubborn, Secretive

Constellation:

SCORPIUS

SCORPIO

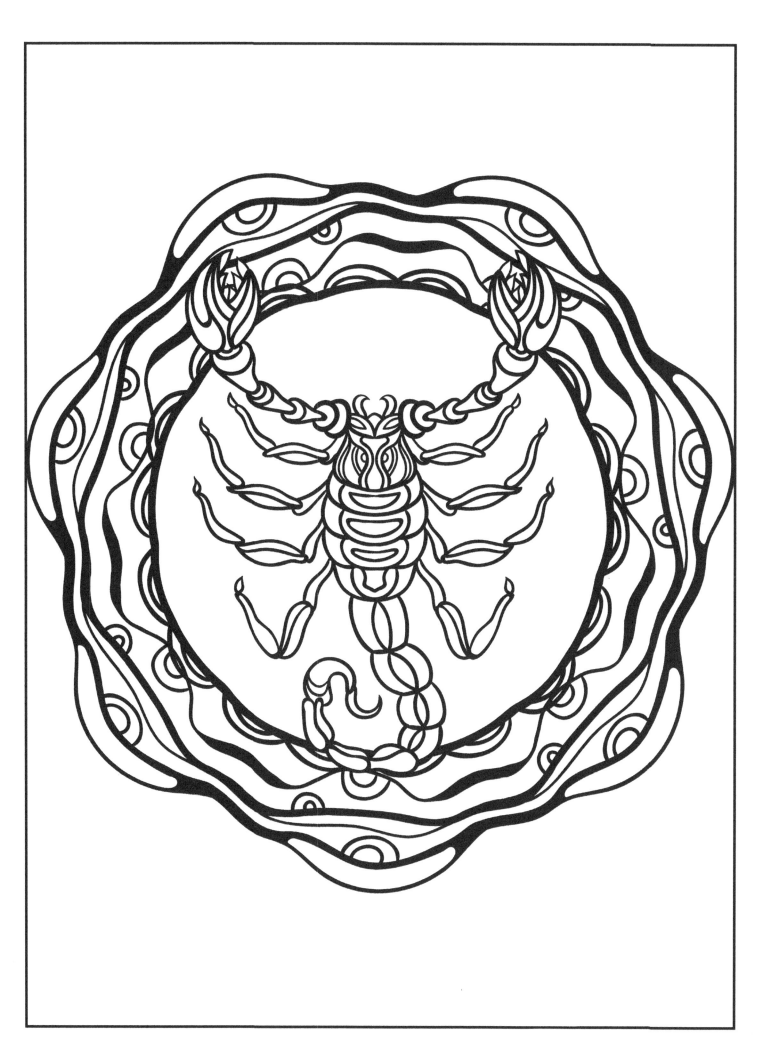

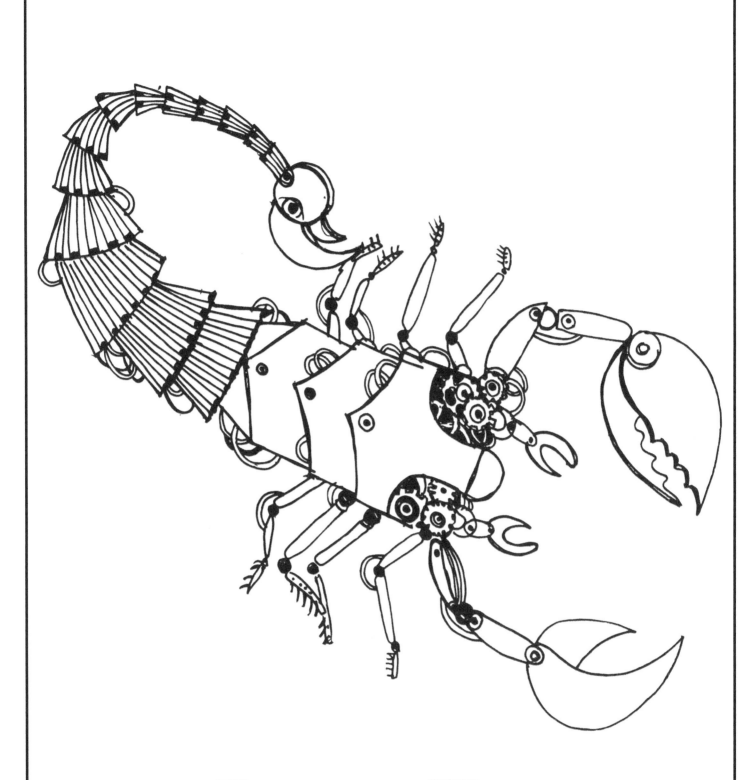

SCORPIO

SCORPIO

Scorpio

Scorpio

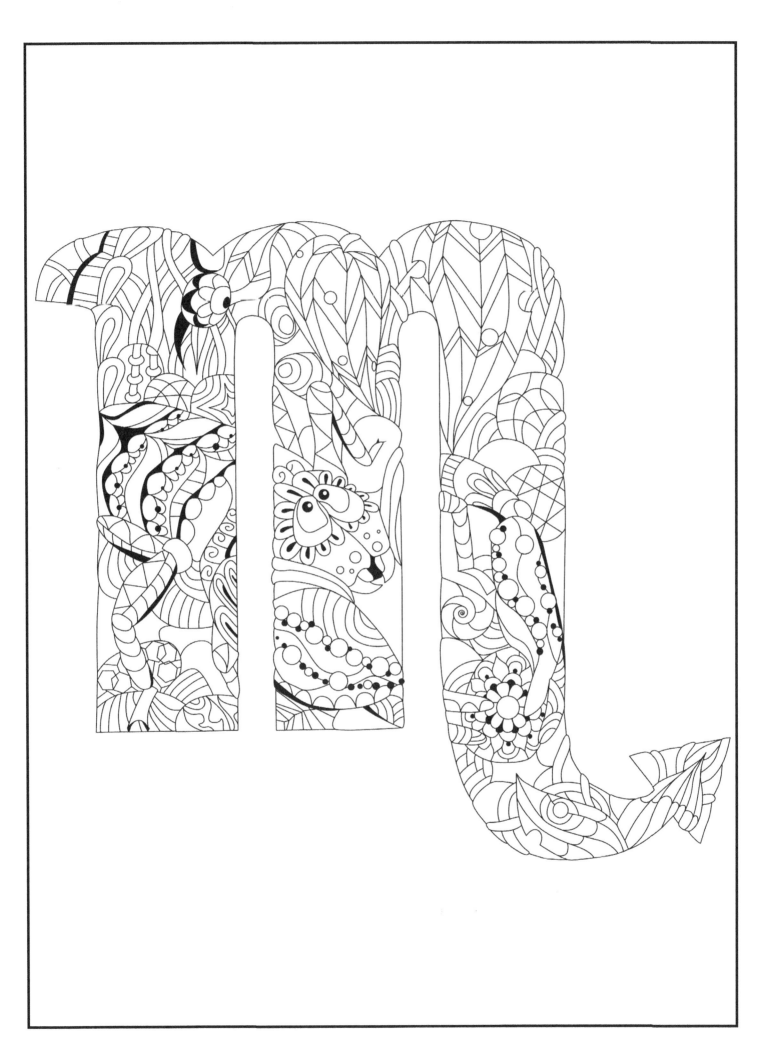

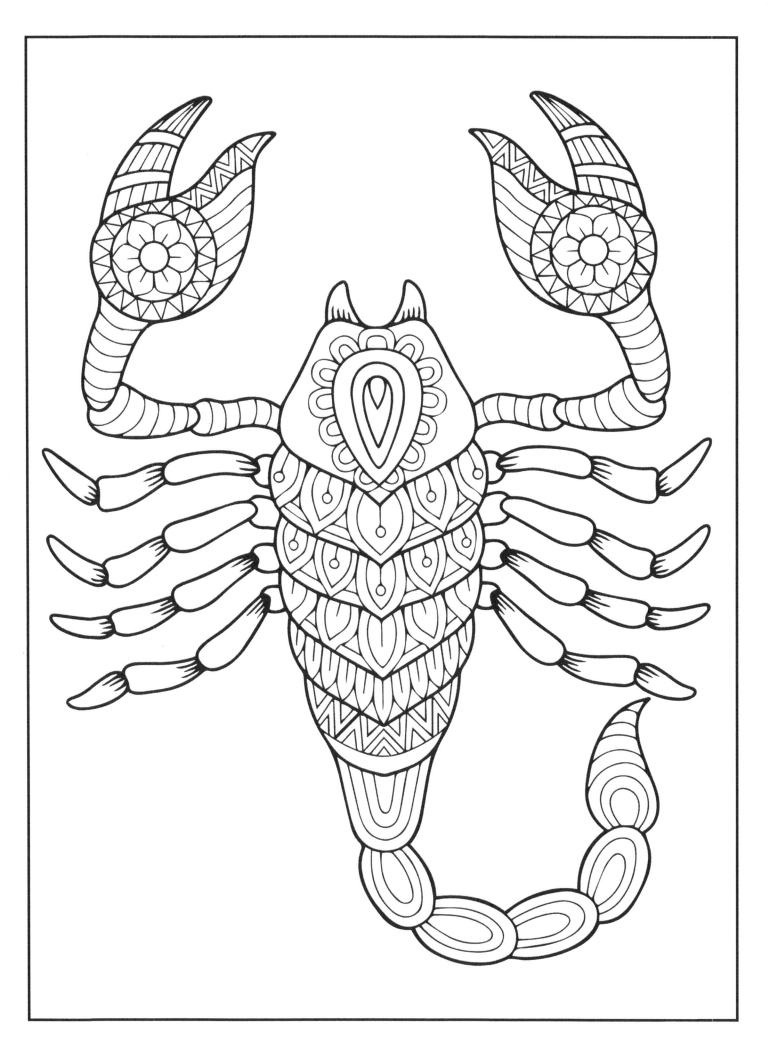

Scorpio

Scorpio

Made in the USA
Middletown, DE
15 March 2023

26858389R00044